Paperback edition first published in the United Kingdom in 2019 by the University of Plymouth Press, Endsleigh Place, Drake Circus, Plymouth, Devon, PL4 8AA, United Kingdom.

ISBN: 9781841024349

© University of Plymouth Press 2019

© INK 2019

Printed and bound by Short Run Press, 25 Bittern Road, Sowton Industrial Estate, Exeter EX2 7LW

INK

JOURNAL 2019

In memory of Dan

Dear Plymouth University,

Re: Dan Hubert Collins, Graduated in September 2017-English + Creative Writing.

My son Dan Hubert Collins tragically passed away on the 28th April 2018. Dan spent three happy years studying at Plymouth University and graduated in September 2017. Myself and Dan's Nan (Katie) are so incredibly proud of our boy.

I enclose a piece of Dan's work 'In Cahoots' and would ask that this be considered for the next 'Ink Journal'

In Cahoots
by
Dan Hubert Collins R.I.P.

Ned Brooks saw the ship
in the distance,
the waves could not
drown out our pleasure.
We raised our glistening arms
in joy, even though we
had lost our girl,
had lost
our voices at
the descent,
into the depths
where all hope
seemed   lost.

To our shame,
We had SkinnED him
from ankle to neck.
His eyes watered,
he had lost his bits.
We had lost our
ship and our
humanity.

(Hysteria)
But then the rabbits came along
a dozen bouncing bunnies sprang
from Mary Toft's private-warren.

Her husband paid the local quack,
Her husband snared the furry pack,
She wept with joy to see her luck
(November 1726)

And each of us in our turn,
Knight, Death and the Devil,
were pulled up to the stern
by stolid German faces.
Ned broke his heart
laughing,
even though
we had lost our
girl and our voices,
laughing.
The Germans were
suddenly
disconcerted.
Ned Brooks saw
Otto von Bismarck
tying his bratwurst
into a chromosome.
He broke his heart,
crying.

(And Mary Toft wept.
She chewed her hair,
her husband, dying,
and a dozen rabbits
sprang
        from
                her)

Chute.

EDITOR'S NOTE

*I*NK 2019 would never have happened but for the unfailing support of my amazing team, particularly Mitch Gregory, Laura Roberts, Georgie Bull and Aimee Matthews who transformed a rough sketch I did on Georgie's kitchen table into an amazing front cover worthy of Jennifer Scampton's captivating artwork which we feel perfectly encapsulates this year's theme of "Changing Climates." I would also like to say an enormous thank you to my boyfriend Glenn Grindrod for ensuring *INK* 2019 was more than just a front cover and for putting up with me when it all got a bit too much and I started muttering about *INK* during my sleep. I would also like to thank Miranda Spicer for inspiring me to run for General Editor in the first place and for introducing me to the Creative Director of Elementum, Jay Armstrong, whose sumptuously-rendered nature journal provided the inspiration for *INK*'s minimalist style.

Congratulations to the winners in each category: Jordan Doyle for Poetry, Amy Potter for Fiction, Jo Higson for Non-fiction and Jennifer Scampton for Illustration and congratulations also to my own personal favourites, Abraham Emdon, Joshua Asker and Sophie Lunnon – Abraham because he writes in a way that is confident and sustained, rich and deeply atmospheric, and Joshua and Sophie because they address profound themes with hopefulness and warmth, two traits that are increasingly rare in this troubled world of ours.

Last but not least, I would like to say a massive thank you to everyone who submitted to *INK* 2019. I recognise that for some of you, *INK* will be only the first step in a long and prosperous career, whereas for others, *INK* will be the only place you will ever be published which is why I was determined to make this as beautiful as possible. Whoever you are, wherever you end up, I hope you will continue to Make Good Art (to quote Neil Gaiman) no matter whether you were lucky enough to get published or not. If you are reading this and your work was rejected, my advice is: don't give up! The reason you were unsuccessful was not because you were rubbish, but because the standard of the work we received was so high – turn over and you'll see what I mean.

Connor Hansford
General Editor

FOREWORD

The climate is changing, the oceans are warming, acidifying, drowning in plastics and losing their breath. Many of the world's cities are suffocating in air pollution -- a killer with around 8 million victims annually. In the meantime we continue to destroy the lungs of this system, our all-mother, Earth. We seem to be forgetting that we need oxygen to breathe, that we ironically, would have never even come into existence if it wasn't for photosynthesising organisms that existed for millennia before our forefathers began to walk up straight. Now, in another twist of irony, we are killing those very beings that gave life to us and thousands of other species. Species which we are pushing further to edge of existence whilst I am writing. As millions of creatures are dying from the consequences of our greedy, selfish and thoughtless acts – the backbones of a capitalist society – some *Homo sapiens* still deny the process that made us who we are, evolution, and the process through which we have made the world what it is today, a changing climate. To me, this shows either the incredible stupidity or incredible selfishness of humanity – and I am not sure which one I find scarier. I suppose it is a toxic mixture of both which reigns: a short sighted, deadly selfishness. Everyone acts in terms of their own short-term best interest. Our compassion is not even enough to provide shelter to members of our own species who have lost everything; or to help people threatened by war or hunger; or simply seeking a better life in "our" countries. Ours since when? Since our forefathers migrated here. Every year we leave thousands of people to die in the Mediterranean, which as the consequence of other human acts, has become a rather dead sea anyway.

Whilst some global leaders still deny

climate change and deny urgently needed action, it is already displacing, starving, drowning people. Over the last few decades we have already extinguished thousands of life-forms that took millions of years to evolve. Whole ecosystems might cease to exist in a couple of decades and some landscapes might never be seen again. We are living on a very precious, unique and astonishingly beautiful planet – it should be an honour for us to be here. Yet we are, not even gradually, taking what makes it so special and beautiful – life.

Climate change is not a fairy-tale, it is not sci-fi, nor fake news - it is a real story. It is us, you and I, and a bunch of lobbyists, CEO's and governors who are writing this story. The current outlook is apocalyptic. The Jane Goodall's, David Attenborough's, Wangari Mathai's, Vandana Shiva's and Greta Thunberg's in this world are not powerful enough to win the battle against the money and power of the oil, carbon and gas lords backed by governments and the current economic system. But let's take a moment to consider, if a sixteen year old rises to global fame standing up for our planet, if young people all over the world are skipping school to demand Climate Justice, if extinction rebels manage to create a big movement within a couple of months, if as little as a 5p charge on single-use plastic bags reduced their usage by over 80% – and ecosystem restorations are actually working, maybe, maybe we still have a chance. Even though this chance, the chance to rewrite the ending to this story, is rapidly diminishing, shouldn't we risk everything to save it?

We have everything to lose.

Laura Prigge
Greenpeace Plymouth
Coordinator

POETRY

GLOBAL MOURNING 3
RAIN 4
BLIND EYES 6
DAYLIGHT LOSING TIME 8
KAMIKAZE 9
PLASTIC SANDS 11
CHANGING FACES 12
NEGLECTING
NATURE'S EMBRACE 13
HERD OF REBEL TREES 14
POLAROID 16

FICTION

TWELVE O'CLOCK   19
THE DARK CLOUD   25
SUNFLOWER OIL   28
MONSTERS IN THE DAWN   33
THE LIGHT AT THE
END OF THE RAMP   35
INHERITANCE   38

NON-FICTION

THE PUFFIN   47
SALT WATER AND
BAILEYS   49
UNTITLED   55
SURVIVING DEATH   59
THE SHADOW MEN   63
THE SHADOW WITH   66
NO CURE

POETRY

ILLUSTRATION: LUKA WRIGHT

GLOBAL MOURNING

JORDAN DOYLE

The breeze teased the canopy;
pleasing nothings whispered.
The warm, tumbling
summer stream
soaked the river's bed.
The yearning earth below
supped the water shed.

Why rub your grubby digits
on Mother's crannied holes?
You've squeezed the
sebum from the pores,
the coal inside her soul.

The stream to steam has
gone –
the Naiades bemoan.
The canopy is withered
now, and Zephyr sighs
alone.

RAIN

EMILY JANET BROWN

Only drizzle,
Then I was drenched in the
downpour.
T-shirts dissolve
And bare legs shiver, purple
tinged.

Welsh umbrella
Not suited to this new climate,
So I discard
You, grasping another cold
hand.

Raindrops trickle
From your cloudy, blue eyes
and I
Jump, splash about
In the puddles. I did not think.

"You'll catch your death
If you get wet" but I did not
Care. Water ran
Down my body: seductive like

Silk. Embrace it.
But sniffles and shudders
remain.
Beware the rain-
Let it tend your garden too.

Now I step out
Into the sun; clouds loom
ahead
But I can smile: new flowers
bloom.

BLIND EYES

KEIRAN POTTER

ILLUSTRATION TIFFANY HARDING

I have cancer in my chest and in my country.
It zigzags through telephone wires and subway carriages.
Its static knows no bounds.
Spreading like a lit match,
Dropped tip first onto a valley of oil.
The flaming jaws crunch down on skulls we cannot see.
Yet we sit and toast marshmallows
On smouldering ashes...

We do so and glance upwards on bare knees. Relinquishing
guilt with false concern
We've seemingly confused prayer with submission,
With ignorance.

Tightropes braided from bloodied scalps
We tread toe to heel.
Before somersaulting off the precipice with a flourish.
The dead bodies of our faceless neighbours
Cushioning our fall

Leaves curl and crack,
Raining down like arsenic from a paint chipped ceiling.
Our teacups are tainted with specs of crimson as we swallow down
the contents in one gulp.

It stings, leaving tongues coated in scarlet and iron. Ignorance or apathy?
We war with ourselves in the confines of speckled mason jars.
By the time we realise the darkness falling on the outside of the glass.
We will have run out of oxygen.

DAYLIGHT LOSING TIME

NANCY DORMAN

The days all began to fade away after he left,
It went from 6pm, to 5pm, to 4pm, to winter.
Each week a shade greyer, blander, than before.
After October, the rain fell daily and it poured
from my hair to my brow bone like God was freshly
anointing me, though it's been years since I believed.
I became October, with falling leaves and shadow,
feeling faithless and so ashamed of just how much
I always miss him.
January ends while I'm in my room listening out.
Downstairs, my best friend shouts at a video game.
The sun reclaims night, scratches of minutes each time.
The rain still falls on my face, brain freeze attacks my nose,
February has yet to prove itself as kinder or less lonesome.
My branches are still bare but contain promise now.
Sometimes, I see stars and I pretend they have power.
I look to them, pick a favourite, close my eyes and I wish
to never be cold again.

KAMIKAZE

KATE LOWMAN

PHOTO: KATE LOWMAN

One last time
the sun kisses the petals.
Ohka-
whose pink confetti showers
rain crimson on its worshippers,
before they are thrust from the tree.

Humble love bites,
tattooed as emblems
on the vessels
destined for the enemy.

Forlorn apologies
inked in letters of tenderness,
promising victory for Japan
in a world they
would not live to see.

Those hopes of glorified memory
shattered.
By surrender of a bereft nation,
the suicide of Ugaki.

He.
The solitary tree:
threatened by the wind,
rooted by the earth.
Sacrificed those who served him
his greatest honour-
his beauty-
for the fortune of his country,
before feeling guilty.
I must kill me.

Banzai-
long live the emperor!
Perishing whispers
of those who accepted
ephemerality.

PLASTIC SANDS

REBECCA GEORGE

Swoosh and splash
Sandcastles stomped by the crashing waves
Hiss and hum
Harbour hopeless dreams of sea life
Crack and creek
Crushed crabs under my feet

Synthetic and sterile
Safer sands made of plastic - humans inbound!
Economically and environmentally
Everyone echoes reuse and recycle
Radically and religiously
Ridiculous reductions of care

The state of the ocean
Is the current affair
A ferry to clearer waters
Cleaner beaches
That could be the future
If people reduced their waste
And stopped making plastic sand

CHANGING FACES

LUKE DANIELS

Ice melts, heat increases, humans aware,
The homeland lessens for the polar bear,
Scientists argue the truth online,
While the Amazon declines slowly vine by vine,
Mother Earth, Mother Earth, are you threatened
yet?
More plastic caught within the fishing net,
We start to lose all the best places,
We caused the earth to have changing faces.

NEGLECTING NATURE'S EMBRACE

SAFFRON GOOD

The world is now burning with rage,
As people fight upon its surface,
Spreading fear and despair,
The cold frost is melting down into tears,
Humanity is the ungrateful child to Mother
Nature,
Neglecting her despite all her gifts and kindness,
She's choked with plastic and fossil fuels,
Tearing down her beauty and jewels,
Crushing flowers and trees,
All in the name of our hatred and greed,
To make our own ugly creations,
Corruption that reaches all nations,
She is dying slowly and cruelly,
She has grown old and needs better care,
But man kind's excuses are old as well,
Denying her of what she deserves,
So the world is neglected and changes shape,
Losing the bright greenery of youth,
As it fades away into grey,
Oceans left overflowing with waste,
So much damage has led her to this state,
So much loss,
Never to be the same again.

HERD OF REBEL TREES

SERGI RUBIO

The sun smiles
down; his reflection winks
And melts on the sea.

The horizon stares
 - with stolid gaze -
The waves tickling
The brooding shore.

On top of the rugged cliff,
A herd of rebel trees
Flee the forest.

Should they flap their branches away
Up to the heavens?
Or should they collect their roots,
Leap off and dive?

Green and wild, they behold
Jets of white-blue spray
Over the edge of the world.

POLAROID

JOSH ASKER

ILLUSTRATION SOPHIE LUNNON

Leaves like snowdrifts line the path to
the badger's sett

Under size two wellies their icebound
frames shatter

Casting crystals like dust motes in the
wake of my Dad

Striding up to the autumn into winter
woods

Searching for the musk filled lair in the
opaline air

FICTION

TWELVE O'CLOCK

BEN HUTTON

The clock on the mantelpiece ticked more and more slowly as its hands reached closer to twelve. "She'll be here soon. She'll be here to see us soon."

The man stared at the door, at its motionless handle. Soon she'd be here.

His finger rose and dropped with each labouring second on the clock, but the door handle didn't twitch. He dropped his gaze towards the sofa beside him. "Budge along a bit will you? Budge along or she'll have no seat."

The clock struck twelve. She wasn't here.

The arms of the chair coiled around the man's waist. His walking cane teased him, resting against the telly that stared back at him. The floor froze to his slippers, with tentacles of ice that dragged him into the deep.

He tugged his blanket up to his belly. Grainy jazz rattled the cabinet's glass like the groan of gunfire.

"You always liked jazz music." The side of the cabinet was plastered with Italian postcards, glowing with a faded sun.

"Remember they played it at the dance? Before they sent me over. The night we said goodbye." His gaze floated inside the cabinet. There were medals in their somewhere. And a dusty beret, lost among other relics.

He glanced towards the clock. Quarter past twelve.

"Did you hear that?"

Footsteps. He switched off the cassette player. "I'll put the telly on for her, how about that?" The footsteps were muffled, like the thud of rain on a distant meadow.

He pecked a finger at his hearing aid.

But the footsteps had gone.

The telly shivered with the drone of a football crowd. "I don't know what all the fuss is about with this game." It must be exciting, being there. But through the screen it was just a bunch of people you couldn't see the faces of. Not even worth keeping your eyes open.

When he opened them again the crowd was gone. So were the footsteps. So was the whole day. The windows were black.

The door creaked open as June finally trudged through. "Hello Dad." Her turtleneck collar was hoisted up to her chin. "Were you talking with someone? I thought I heard voices." Her eyes hovered and sailed around the room as she spoke. "Anyway, I've got your paper here."

The newspaper smelt so fresh, like autumn timber within the shade of a forest. The room became as bright as an Italian beach.

He gazed at the sofa beside him. His throat clogged. The sand blew from his imagination, down the gullet of an hourglass.

June's eyes twitched towards the clock.

The man's gaze meandered into the cabinet. Something in there was watching him.

"Look at that, June. In there."

"It's too much of a jumbled mess in there to see a thing."

His tendons burned and his knees clanked. His tongue brushed his lips with sourness. His mouth inflated with hot breath.

"Dad, sit back down!"

His blanket tumbled to his feet as he seized his cane. "Just take a look, June." He shuffled towards the cabinet, and its twinkling door swung open with a click. Damp wool and plastic oozed into the room.

"Here we are." He clasped the arm of a porcelain doll. It was a tacky old thing really. But then it always had been. The threads of its dress were yellowed and peeling apart, but its eyes still glistened. One of its feet was a cracked stump, but the other was bundled in a white tattered shoe.

"Blimey Dad, no wonder you keep that thing buried in there." She recoiled and buried her nose in her hand.

The man turned his head back towards the sofa. "Remember when we bought this?"

June tapped his shoulder.

The man shook his head. "You were only a child when we bought this for you, June."

She plucked the doll from his grip. "I didn't even know you had it." She skimmed her thumb over the jagged ankle.

"Look, we kept this for a reason." He stroked a gold ring on his finger. "You know everything we keep in the cabinet means something to us. We can't have it all out on show. You know I'd find that difficult."

She stroked the white shoe. "I'm sorry, Dad." The pale leather was thin and soft, but hardened by the doll's foot inside. "I just haven't seen it in all these years." Her eyes froze, and the doll's clothing rustled as she breathed.

In the silence, the clock ticked like a war drum.

June blinked. "I ought to let you get ready for dinner."

"Just wait a minute." He stole the doll from June's grip. "You didn't see what I wanted to show you." He gripped the white shoe between his finger and thumb, giving it a tug.

June snatched the doll by the shoulders, but the man still had a firm grip. His face boiled. "It won't come off!"

"Stop being so ridiculous, Dad!"

There was a rasping sound. The man stumbled back onto his cane as he released the doll. His eyeballs retreated into the caverns of his skull. "I tore it." He raised a hand over his eyes.

"What on Earth has gotten into you?" She placed the doll back with a ceramic jingle, and herded the man back to his chair.

"I just wanted to show you it properly." He stroked the shreds of leather in his hand. "It's your baby shoe. I suppose your old doll's foot was the only place we thought we could put it." He looked away from June, and shifted his words towards the sofa. "You gave it to me on that night we said goodbye. And I kept it with me, everywhere I went." The man's nostrils flared with every strained breath. He never stopped staring at the sofa. "We've kept it here ever since." He brushed his eyelids closed. "Since that night we said goodbye."

June looked towards the sofa, at nothing more than empty space.

THE DARK CLOUD

ABIGAIL PURVIS

"Quickly Alessia! You don't have time to pack – we have to go!" my mother yelled. I hate it when she yells.

I wipe the beads of sweat from my forehead onto my sleeve, which was still slightly damp from the reminisce of my previous wipe. I roll onto my toes to grab the final tin from the back of the cupboard. Mushy peas. *Great. My hopes of surviving the next couple of days rely on various goods including baked beans, kidney beans, coconut milk and… mushy peas.*

"Alessia!" my mother snaps.

"Mother!" I snap back.

"We have to go!"

"Go where mum? Where are we going to go?"

"The city… for pickups." she said, full of false hope.

"Right yes, the British government are really coming to the rescue. They couldn't even leave the EU! You seriously think they would be able escape the end of the world?"

I looked to my mother who was staring at me blankly. I could see that all the purpose and importance had drained from her. She no longer had authority and power over me, she no longer had a routine or ambitions for the future. All she could do was pray that someone, and apparently that someone was the government, was coming to save us. Life was no longer as we knew it. It's from that realisation that I predicted why her eyes began to glisten and her blinking speed increased significantly.

I fill up a final water bottle and put it in my 65-litre hiking rucksack and hand my mother one for hers, which I had also packed.

"Let's go." I say, hiding a groan, bending my knees as I bounce the rucksack onto my back.

Everyone else in Edinburgh seemed to have the same idea as my mother. The whole of the Royal Mile was crowded full of anxious people awaiting further advice and instruction. We had all received the same message about an hour ago: Evacuate. It is time to go: the end has come.

I watch the hysteria increase and resonate throughout the crowd. We all knew it but chose to ignore it. No help is coming, we are on our own. I reassuringly squeeze my mother's hand and I look her straight in the eye. I wait for her to focus on me and I say to her seriously and calmly; "We should head North."
"Alessia, we should wait. They might come." Then with some final hope she said with a weird mix of excited doubt, "The government might issue some more advice?"
"What's left of the government you mean?" I reply.
"That's not helpful. They might have cars, or lorries, or… or something. They can take us to safety."

I haven't seen cars since I was a little girl, probably about eight years ago. They had all been destroyed in a final attempt to save the planet. Everyone had ignored the pleas to reduce transport-based emissions, so the enviro party issued a law for all cars to be destroyed and their parts recycled. The importation of diesel and petrol were also prohibited. But it was too late, for the last eight years climate change just continued to increase rapidly. Winter became unimaginable and summer became hotter than ever.

Six months ago, Australia's wildfires became so extreme and uncontrollable that it is believed that it spread across the country. Everything burnt to nothing. There has been no communication since it first started and it is assumed that its either because it all got destroyed or everyone is dead, or both.

Europe was next, the storm is said to be as damaging as a hurricane and as frightening as the World War II bombings. The storm has brought about a new sort of oxygen compound that contains too many toxins, sort of like the smog in the early twentieth-century. No one knows for sure, its all speculation, but those who have gotten near it have died. And now this smoggy air cloud was heading for England and Scotland.
It's been four months since America was flooded and submerged, thought to be the result of the final polar ice caps melting.
"Let's get the bikes" I say. "The bikes, Mum. We can get as far North as possible and then when we hear that the storm has hit the Channel Islands and then Cornwall, we can head up nice and high in the hills and hope for clean oxygen up there"
"But help might be coming." she protests
"Who is coming to help us? The government? The Russians? No. And if they do, where are they going to take

everyone? The whole world is collapsing. Nowhere is safe."

"Alessia, we have to hope."

"I'm trying Mum. I'm hoping there is help in the mountains. I'm hoping we can make it that far. I'm hoping we can find a bothy or use the tent I packed and ration ourselves on what we have with us- ", even if that is mushy peas, I think, "-for as long as possible and hopefully make it through the next few days"

"But what if help does come, and we miss it?"

"There is no help!" I yell, causing the stirring of the anxious people in front of us to panic even more. I continue regardless; "When are you going to get it into your head that no one is coming to pick us up in a space ship and take us to another planet." I pause, waiting for her to listen properly. "We are stuck in the mess of humanity's own destruction."

I pull on my Mum's hand and drag her silently back to what was once our house, and there I pull out the bikes from the garage.

After one final glance back at Edinburgh, I put my hand on Mum's shoulder and try to reassure that we are doing the right thing: "There is no Planet B Mum".

SUNFLOWER OIL

NATHAN BOWEN

ILLUSTRATION: SUMMER CHURCHILL

A partially submerged caravan lays upside-down. Beige aluminium buckled and twisted. A sign floats past in the rising water. Faded blue letters against a white background. Three Oaks Holiday Park.

It rains. Intense and relentless; raindrops the size of gravel. Clouds dark as charcoal churn in the turbulent sky. Lightning flashes; blue-white lines crooked like the veins of a leaf. A crag of rock rises from the hillside to the East of the former holiday park. Water gushes down grey rock to fill the valley below. In a cave deep within, Adam shivers as he listens to the wind howl through gaps above his head. He looks at Harry, watches as he uses his finger to make shapes in the dirt. The candle quivers in the breeze and sends shadows flickering across the damp walls. Adam nods to Megan. 'It's time' he mouths. She nods back, takes a seat next to Harry.

"Hey Harry." She says, his finger stops playing in the dirt as he looks up.
"Yeah?"
"Will you go see how high the water is?" She asks.
Harry's nose twitches. He looks at her, his lips press tight.
"Check the water level?" He repeats as if he'd not heard her properly the first time.

"Yes." She answers.

"You think it could be this high already?"

"Hopefully not, but it would be worth checking. Nobody's been out for days."

"Okay. If you really want me to."

Harry stands, holds his hands against the the roof of the cave and stretches. He looks down to Megan, back to Adam and across to Steve who's sat on the damp mattress they dragged in all those months ago. "I'll go check the water then." He says, uncertainly.

He leaves through the side entrance, walking slowly, using his hands to guide him along the rough stone wall.

"Quick." Adam says.

The three of them move with a sense of urgency. Steve opens a drawer in the bedside cabinet; the only piece of furniture they'd managed to rescue before the water got too high. He rummages through their meagre possessions, rushing back with a small tin and a thin blue-red striped candle. Adam lights the candle, drips wax on the tin lid and fixes it in place. Megan gets a pillowcase and lays it on the floor. They arrange the tin in the centre. Adam looks to Megan, she nods with approval.

"Perfect." She whispers.

They hear footsteps.

"It's up another two meters. The caravans on the far hill are almost gone." Harry voice echoes into the main chamber.

"Happy birthday to you. Happy birthday to you. Happy birthday, dear Harry. Happy birthday to you." Adam, Steve and Megan sing together as Harry rounds the corner. Their voices are rough, unharmonised and out of time.

Harry stops.

"What's this?" His eyes flick between the three of them.

"Well we didn't have a cake." Adam says.

Harry picks the tin up and reads the label aloud.

"Tuna chunks in sunflower oil." A high-pitched squeal seeps

from his throat. "Tuna? But... I... how... I don't know what to..." His mouth hangs wide open.

"We know it's your favourite." Megan says. "The one thing you miss most from before."

"But, how did you..."

"Steve found it. Two weeks ago, scavenging through one of the chalets before the water got up that far."

"And you've kept it all this time. But...Wh-" The words lodge in Harry's throat. He swallows. His eyes stare intently at the tin.

"Well, we knew your birthday was soon and we wanted it to be special." Megan says.

Harry blinks, eyes shimmering beneath a film of moisture. He rubs a finger over the corners of his eyes.

"Well go on then." Megan says. "Blow out the candle and make a wish."

"Can I wish for sunshine?" He asks, the lightness in his voice making it sound like a joke.

"Please do." Megan says. "And wish for hair straighteners too."

Harry raises an eyebrow. He kneels down, puts the tin back on the pillowcase, takes a deep breath and blows the candle out. Adam and Steve clap. Megan pats him on the back.

Harry takes the candle off the tin.

"It's... It's a party candle." He says as if this is the most absurd thing in the world.

"I found birthday napkins too, but I had to use them when I got the runs."

"Alright Steve." Megan says. "A bit too much detail mate."

Suddenly the cave is full of laugher and for the briefest of moments it's as if everything is normal. The laughter fades. Harry pulls the lid off the tin. For a long while nobody says anything. They listen to the wind that blows through cracks in the rock, the drips that fall incessantly from above. Adam stares at the tuna and thinks of the pretty dark-haired girl that worked in the sandwich shop by the beach. He never got to ask her name.

"We should share." Harry says placing the tin down between them.

"You first." Adam gestures.

Hurry digs his fingers in and shoves them in his mouth. Sunflower oil drips from his lips.

"Ummm." His eyes squeeze shut. "Heavenly." Harry passes the tin to Megan who takes a pinch and hands it on.

"Cracking birthday." Harry says. "What time is everyone else arriving?"

The cave fills with laugher once more.

MONSTERS IN THE DAWN

AMY POTTER

The wind howls, piercing the silence that surrounds us. My body is pulled in each direction but my hold on the branch doesn't falter. I have done this a million times, and I hope I will do it a million more, but our future has never been more uncertain. The expanse of space before me has never looked so different. Our land changes constantly, but never so drastically or so permanently.

Standing, the branch shakes more feverishly and I lean forward, take one deep breath, close my eyes and jump. As the ground rushed up to meet me, I grab a branch just in time. And I leap and swing, and I leap and swing again and again. Racing through the trees so fast they blur together in a tornado of green. I know these trees better than I know my own family, this one has weaker branches, that one allows you to swing further than another. That tree is home to a family of woodpeckers and that one in the distance is…well it was, the tallest tree in the entire forest. But this morning it fell. No, it didn't fall, it was taken from us. In less than a minute, the king of the forest, the tree that was the first to reach the sun and has stood tall for hundreds of years, was callously stolen.

First you hear the engines, they scream and shout, monsters in the dawn that creep up and steal away what is ours. Their black smoke claims the sky so the difference between day and night becomes indistinguishable. The birds left months ago, they saw it coming with their far-reaching eyes and their wings that can carry them miles in a moment. What I would give for a pair in wings. At least I can leap and jump out of the line of fire, our trees are not so lucky. With our goal in sight, we press forwards. Racing faster each time, we make it a game so the young ones can't see our fear. We whoop and holler as if we are simply playing tag. On occasion I fool myself too, thinking perhaps this is all a dream and we will wake up from this nightmare. But that is yet to happen, and my hope that it will becomes smaller each day that passes.

We must do this more often now, we can't stay in one place for long. The monsters are deeply unforgiving and even more unrelenting. The forest is our home but with every day that passes our home becomes smaller and smaller. The perpetuating decline in space pushes us further north. The weather is getting worse, the food is getting scarce. It scares me. It scares me that there is absolutely nothing that we can do to stop this. I can scream and shout and howl at the yellow beasts, but they speak a language that is foreign to me. A language that is inept of emotion, compassion and feeling. I hope it stops soon, because if it doesn't, we will have no home left.

THE LIGHT AT THE END OF THE RAMP

SERGI RUBIO

Nil opened his eyes and saw the sun dawning through the window; his heart quickened its beat as his bleary eyes adjusted to the sight of the spherical fire, rising over the purple horizon. *Ja som a Barcelona?* Thought Nil, feeling his stomach shrink and the pressure blocking his ears as the plane spiralled its way down in large circles. The window at his side was like a small TV screen: now showing images of the Catalan sun sprawling orangey arms over the Mediterranean Sea; now shifting the channel to show the Costa Daurada, the Golden Coast and the city of Barcelona emerging from the darkness.

When the plane was safely bestowed on the land, the captain's voice informed that the temperature was 24 degrees Celsius and wished a lovely stay in Barcelona to all passengers. His ears unblocked and relieved, Nil grabbed his rucksack and smiled back at the cabin crew lady bidding farewell to everyone. He stepped out of the plane, and headed to Passport Control wondering if he had really slept all the way through. It was a fourteen hour flight.

He remembered that dinner was served by the cabin crew, shortly after taking-off from a Sri Lankan Airport; chicken curry, couscous, hummus with pita bread, carrot sticks, and a sweet Arabic pastry for dessert. Delicious. Shame, it didn't come in very large amounts. He couldn't recall at what point he fell asleep after the meal, but as he approached the Passport Control cabin he thought it was better to focus on not speaking Catalan to the Spanish police officer and risk a fine. He unzipped the exterior pocket of his rucksack and took out his passport. The border officer let him through, paying no heed to him or the document in his hand.

He checked the screen: EK358 –

Belt 13. The only suitcase on the spinning belt was his. He grabbed the suitcase and headed to the car-park. The whole terminal seemed unusually dim and quiet. He tried ringing Pol: no answer. He heaved a sigh and went to validate his parking ticket. Zero? *No pot ser…* He reinserted the ticket twice or three times more, thinking that the machine was not operating properly, but the device insisted that the amount due was zero. Well, perhaps it was his lucky day; and with a weird sense of joy, as if he had won an illegal lottery prize, he called the lift and the doors opened at that very instant.

Once in the lift, he couldn't recall on what floor he had left his car. A halo of heat suddenly crowned his head. He massaged his temples hoping that the memory of him parking his car would flash in his mind. It didn't. He decided to hit number four as he usually parked on the top floor. He checked every single slot, but his car wasn't there. It's got to be on level three then. He headed downstairs and as he did on level four he checked every single spot, without any luck. The air became scarce and stale as his mouth became dry. There were two more levels to check. He popped an Orbit mint in his mouth. Who would steal an old Nissan Leaf, anyway?

He took the stairs down to level two. Nothing. Then to level one. Nothing there either. He tried ringing Pol again: still no answer. He refrained the impulse to smash his iPhone 4 against the wall, but he hit the button to call up the lift instead. The parking was brimming with Audis, BMWs, Mercedes; he even spotted a Tesla Model S in level three…

No, no one would steal an old electric car like his, even leaving the doors open and the motor on. He must have missed the spot. He would start all over again from level four. It took ages before the lift-doors opened. When they finally did, and he was about to hit number four, his face went pale. There was also a number five? How could he not have noticed it before? He hit the goddammed button not knowing whether to feel hope or shame. His heartbeat raced when the lift-door dinged open. He clenched his fist, his thumbs rubbing against the other fingers, almost praying for his car to be there. No other cars were around, no other people coming in or getting out, but he didn't care; it was there, his car was there! He put his hands on his knees and gasped as if finally springing out of the water, from the depths of the abyss. He shot at it with the remote key-car, before it vanished again: the old Nissan Leaf flashed its four blinkers.

He threw his suitcase in the boot, placed his rucksack on the rear seat, but when he buckled his seatbelt... a weird emotion started to build up from within. Albeit, he was safe now, inside his car, ready to go home, Nil struggled to constrain a sudden urge to cry. He wiped his eyes with the back of his hand; then, he started the motor, turned the lights on and manoeuvred the vehicle out of the spot. He switched on the radio, but no station could be tuned, just that noise of leaking air. He clenched the steering wheel with both hands and hit the pedal towards the exit. The wheels squeaked when he took the turn down to level four. He heaved a sigh as if trying to make room for more patience.

He cut through the darkness towards level three. The urge to burst into tears, harder and harder to constrain. Nil drove on to level two, panting as if the air was too thick to reach the lungs. He kept going down to level two; the whole building was getting darker and darker at every turn. Then he carried on to level one grinding his teeth and almost holding his breath. Finally, at the ground level, Nil squinted at a very bright light, rolling towards him like a great ball of white fire. A torrent of fresh air flowed down his nostrils and cleansed his lungs. Once more, he wiped his eyes with the back of his hand, pressed the button to make the window go down and inserted the ticket in the machine at his side, with a trembling hand.

"Gràcies i bon viatge," said the machine on a little screen. The barrier opened, Nil hit the pedal, wheels screeching with relief and he could not hold it anymore: heading to the light at the end of the ramp, he burst into tears with all the fury from his lungs.

"Waah! waah! waah!"

Nasi held Nina's hand and kissed her forehead.

"Empeny, Nina, empeny!" Instructed Aloma.

"Waah! Waah! Waah!"

Aloma knew that the child was healthy and full of energy by the way that cute little thing was crying. She cut the umbilical cord and wrapped the infant with a towel.

"És un nen!" Said Aloma handing the infant to Nina.

The young mum cuddled her baby boy close. The wailing ceased. A luminous smile blossomed in his plum tiny face, turning the dim little room into a fountain of joyous light.

INHERITANCE

ABRAHAM EMDON

ILLUSTRATION: ABRAHAM EMDON

The winters were long here; longer than you, or perhaps even your ancestors who lived through the great ages of ice, could imagine. It was hard to survive in such harsh conditions, and harder still to find comfort on those endless winter nights. And so it was, as the biting winds howled around the caves and hide tents where hardy folk sat out hard winters, that their bored children would creep up to the elders huddled by the fire and beg of them:

"Tell us a story, grandmother! Tell us about the Ancient Ones, who built glass towers and flew about on dragons!"

And the elder, who by our standards today was not really very old at all, would smile grimly and reply: "Very well, little ones. Gather your sisters and mothers. I will tell you a story about the Ancient Ones, so that you might learn of their folly."

So the children would gather, with their sisters and mothers, to listen. The menfolk were out in the dark, caring for the animals that sustained the tribe through the cold; but they, too, knew the stories of the Ancient Ones, for their own elders had told them over campfires many years before, and theirs before that, unto time eternal. And they all knew of the mighty and ruinous edifices that they passed in their yearly migration from north to south and back again, great skeletons of rusting iron that jutted from ice sheets and shallow ocean beds, and the footprints of vast cities that their circuitous route skirted around or through depending on the season.

"Listen, sons and daughters of man," the elder would say, although she would not, of course, be speaking English. You would not recognise the language she spoke, for it had no basis in any root language that constitute the foundations of our various tongues today. "Listen to the history of a people who are dead now."

And they would listen to the stories that the elder told, clustered closely around the crackling fire, as the biting winds of the long winter howled outside their caves and hide tents:

"Once, the Great Mother teemed with life; endless green covered the land, which was almost devoid of ice and snow, as plagues us today. Animals roamed the earth in abundance: deer, oxen and horses, which travelled in vast herds and grazed on boundless meadows of emerald grass; rabbits, squirrels and fowl, who hopped about foraging for berries in the undergrowth and safety of the trees; and tigers, wolves and the mighty eagle on high, that plucked their food from among the lesser animals, but only as needed - for they were not propelled by greed, only survival.

"Then came another creature, and they were kings among all animals, for with their weapons and tools no other animal could compete -- not even Tiger, who was stronger in body and claw, but weaker in cunning. These were humans, our forebears, and they could do things that no other animal could dream of; and they did.

"Indeed, such was their dominance that mankind spread quickly, like a blight on the land; chopping and burning the Great Mother's forests to build their homes and fuel their fires; destroying any predator who could cause them harm, eating and enslaving the animals that roamed, hopped and flew, that their people could enjoy fresh meat every day - killing in such numbers that the very cycle of life and death was disrupted and countless species disappeared forever. These are creatures that you and I, young ones, will never see and cannot begin to envision."

At this, the children's faces would light up as they tried to imagine what kinds of animals once roamed the land before the calamity of man.

"But they wanted more." the elder would continue with sorrow in her voice, "They pillaged the Mother's land for precious stones to wear about their necks and ores to build more tools and weapons to kill. They built great cities of glass on riverbanks for their vast numbers to live in, which turned Mother's once clear waters into cesspools of human waste; and they poured so much smoke into the skies from their manufactories, horseless carts and flying machines that their children choked on putrid air and the Earth grew hot under a blanket of poison.

"And, alas, there were those among the billions who saw what humanity had borne; who wished to reverse the damage done to the Great Mother and restore balance to nature; but they were ignored, and they were too late, for mankind had sealed their doom long before.

"Then there came the great storms, the hurricanes which blew away cities; the floodwaters that washed away their coastlines; the eruption of the Fiery God across the Great Sea, and the age of ice that followed, that killed them in billions, as the ash the God had spewed blocked out the sun. This was Mother's punishment for the destruction that man had wrought; through water, storm, fire and ice, she struck down their mighty glass towers, froze their crops to mush, and washed away their civilisation like you would wash the fleas off your back.

"When the age of ice subsided, our ancestors came back from the southern lands to whence they had retreated. But they had forgotten how to build their great cities; how to burn fuel in colossal foundries and turn stone into machinery that would allow us to grow and cover the world with ease; and, indeed, how to fly, on dragons made of steel.

"And they did not want to know, for those things had destroyed their ancestors and the land with them.

"This is the lesson our forefathers left for us, O children who walk among ruins of grand cities! Respect life, respect the Great Mother, and remember; it is better to live in harmony with the Earth than to seek domination over it."

And the children would remember the lesson, unto time
eternal.

NON-FICTION

ILLUSTRATION: SIAN ROLSTON

THE PUFFIN

JO HIGSON

The first time I sighted a live puffin was around the Western Isles - a rocky outcrop of the Isles of Scilly. I was with my parents and brother on a seal-watching trip aboard a crusty open boat, with the smell of diesel fumes from the on-board engine mixing with the salty scents of the ocean swell. Although the day was warm, out at sea it was chilly, and we all had itchy handknits under our meant-to-be-waterproof cagoules.

The boat's captain skilfully used the grinding forward and return gears to keep the boat as steady as he could whilst enabling us to sweep the coastline with our second-hand binoculars, and still avoiding the treacherous rocks. On a previous trip we had seen the planks ripped open by a momentary clash with an unseen submerged crag, and while the women and children were precariously passed over to a neighbouring boat on a similar tour,

the men stood at one side to keep the gaping wound above the waterline while the skipper headed back over open sea to St. Mary's.

We came around the headland and suddenly there they were: tens of red-beaked, clown-faced, bulbous birds communing on the rocks. But they were so small. That wasn't what I was expecting - and apparently that is a common reaction.

The average puffin is only about fifteen inches tall: you could pop one in your handbag. Perhaps it is the close-up photographs that are often taken, with no indication of scale to spoil the potentially award-winning shot, which form our view of the size of a puffin. I did a quick straw poll of the people I was working with one day, and the majority opinion was that they were not dissimilar in size to a small penguin.

It is something about their stocky

build, black and white plumage and large colourful beaks that attracts us to puffins. It could also be that we project onto them our own cultural values and love the fact that they form long-term pair bonds. Both parents incubate the egg and feed the chick before it fledges and heads out to sea, only to return around five years later when it is ready to breed.

As with other "cute" birds and animals, owls being a good example, they are currently a fashionable motif used to decorate numerous household items from mugs to bedlinen, cufflinks to tea towels. I confess to having a delicate porcelain mug with puffins around the base holding balloons in their beaks. I don't remember where I bought it, but it could well have been on a nostalgic wave following that first encounter on the Scillies.

In Iceland, where they are most numerous, puffins are included in many myths, sagas and children's tales. Their feathers are worn as regalia at official occasions; they are celebrated on postage stamps, and as a national mascot: but they also eat them. Puffin meat is part of the national diet and is commonly featured on hotel menus. The fresh heart of a puffin eaten raw is a traditional Icelandic delicacy! I don't think I'll be seeking out that delicacy anytime soon. I'll stick to my mug.

In other areas of the world, puffins are revered: in coastal Alaska and North America, the Inuit and Native American tribes see puffins as having power over storms and other weather. If that were true, however, you would imagine they might have put a halt to the climate change which is impacting on their food supplies and threatening their very existence. Since 2015 puffins have been listed as a "vulnerable" population, meaning they face a high risk of extinction in the wild.

This is heart-breaking.

SALT WATER AND BAILEYS

JORDAN LEWIS

ILLUSTRATION ELOISE LEVIEN

*T*empestuous *power, reckless in its cerulean dance across the shoreline.*

The voice of the Earth-shaker, a booming roar that puts the terror of gods into mortal souls.

As restless as long nights, heartbeat reverberating in your eardrums in a rhythmic pulse, pulse, pulse against the skin.

Something alive and uncooperative, thrashing against its confines desperate to escape.

My notebook stares up at me with contempt. Discomfort across its pages as it asks:

"Are you even talking about the sea anymore?"

This trip to a Cornish beach, that I can't remember the name of, on a date somewhere in January, is supposed to be a trip to get me inspired and thinking positively about the next term. So, while Dave and I are here I've set myself the challenge of writing some atmospheric imagery of the sea. Some imagery that I actually like. But instead, the tide is pulling me out and setting me adrift on memories I usually keep a careful distance from.

The seaweed green of the fields outside my window flood my view. Rolling out of sight and back towards the coast. It is a far cry from the calming blue I'd left behind in Devon. The room Mum has set aside for me here in Gloucestershire is sparse of detail: a bed, a chair, a desk and the window, filled with green waves that are entirely wrong. I was twelve years old and cooped up inside despite the fact it was summer. Mum was downstairs, either unpacking or on the phone again.

"This was a move for the best," she would say to me. "Here we will be closer to family." She tried to convince me that this was a homecoming. But it didn't feel like coming home.

Dave is walking in the distance, stepping on sea foam and giving me space to write. We are the only ones on this beach, apart from the gulls that swing overhead and scream at the horizon, trying to include themselves in the symphony of white noise rolling off the tide. Dave does not scream at the water rushing to meet his feet, but each footprint in the sand does speak volumes.

TV static with the volume dial turned up to maximum and the bass boosted. You can feel it beating against your palm when you lay a hand on the speakers.

This metaphor is not quite right either.

Having been in Gloucestershire for almost seven months, I had figured out that inside a building the green waves of the fields did not have the same overwhelming presence. Today however, there is a storm brewing in Mum's head, and as I stand beside her in the local shop, inside does not feel safe. The thunder of the Baileys bottle as it rumbled towards the cashier was almost deafening. I try and smile like the cashier is, calm and distant.

Beep beep. There it went with a crack of lightning, into a bag and off to a cupboard I should not have known about, to join another already there. I smile, and ignore the change in the weather. Any worries were pushed away, to be hidden in pages and ink later, because

who would listen to the concerns of a twelve-year-old girl so far from home?

My pen stops as I realise I've written that last thought down, instead of letting it be. I give the notebook a scathing glare, and it looks back innocently. The waves crash as I cross out the nervous thoughts of the child I once was. I continue writing:

Sheets of glass smash against the shingle in a destructive performance, but my mind searches for what is behind the curtains.

This image is nice, but the second clause changes the sentence's meaning from a simple metaphor about the waves, to how I internalise and question everything around me instead of facing my problems. I don't even know what I'm looking for. Closure that would settle me like calm seas on a clear night? An outlet for the storm in me that wants to wreck ships? A reason for why I still feel like a terrified twelve-year-old, shouting at my Mum as she drunkenly cries down the phone to my Dad about what a horrible brat of a child I am?

I'm not entirely sure how I got from my Mum's to my Aunt's, and from there to my Dad's back in Devon. All I remember is the car sailing through the traffic of the M5, throat aching and hands shaking as I watched the rolling seaweed green fields out the window. I was filled with an emotion that has no name, but roils beneath the skin like hatred and trembles in the chest like grief.

When we got to Dad's, however, I was relieved to see blue waves out my window again. It almost felt like a homecoming.

And with that, the tide rolls me back onto a Cornish beach that I can't remember the name of, on a date somewhere in

January. I look out one final time into the shades of blue that I cannot force a single metaphor to fit. I'm close enough that I could walk right in and drown in it.

Instead, I stand from the damp rock I have been sat on, and walk away. Dave is stepping on sea foam, and my notebook is tired of me.

UNTITLED

DAN SEWELL

My cat doesn't believe in climate change. Although technically that's only because she has no concept of it, because she's a cat. It's a worry she just doesn't have.

Her life is pretty mundane from a human perception. Leaving the street for her, would be like leaving the planet for us. The only responsibility she has is not to urinate or defecate in the house. The rest of the time she just lazes about and does nothing. And we praise her for it. But what about me, a student with responsibilities? I have rent to pay, assignments to complete by deadlines, reading, caring for my cat. Do I get praise for this? Do I really need to answer?

Unlike my cat, I do believe in climate change. Not just the actual climate-changing climate change, but the climate of life changing. Unlike my cat, my life does change. I'm a student for one. That's a pretty big change from college life. Back then if you said bibliography, I would say biblio-what. Ah, nostalgia. As a third-year student, another change is on the horizon. I don't yet know what I'm going to be doing, but whatever I do decide, it will be a huge change presumably. It's hasn't happened yet. I'm sitting on a cliff edge, facing the unknown fate below. A strange and colourful fate, it looks a lot like a painting. I haven't the foggiest what it means. So, I do what any sane being would do in my situation when stuck in such a predicament. I order pizza.

The delivery driver fails to apply the brakes, falling down below. Luckily, I managed to grab the pizza off the moped just in the nick of time. I love big pizzas with cheesy crusts and lots of toppings. I eat the whole thing. Young people are always blamed for everything. It somehow is directly our fault that we were born in the technological age. It was also our fault when our parents introduced said technology to us at a young age. Oh, a Nintendo, that will shut him up for a few hours. When my grandad was a child, him and his mates paid money to a rich neighbour so they could go and watch *Robin Hood* on a tiny black and white tele. But when I buy the latest *Planet of the Apes* film in stunning HD, then I'm only doing it because it's in some online store and I have no concept of the value of money. I should've just asked if my neighbour had a copy. I'm always getting harassed by people I know on what I plan to do after my third year. It's annoying. I'm guessing that they have the idea that this sort of decision can and should be made within a day. Then I knock the hammer against wood and that's that. Ah, simplicity. Change takes time. Time to get used to for one. When I get to the end of a long boxset, it's difficult to move on. It's like I need time to mourn the characters and the end of their storylines. Change in life is a difficulty, it's one of the luxuries of being a cat.

Whatever I choose to do, someone will surely have a problem with. Stay at Uni: You're wasting your time on education. Become a writer: You'll never get actually published unless you're lucky. Become a journalist: You shouldn't be writing for that particular outlet. Become a YouTuber: That's not a real job because it didn't exist in my day. Work a 9-5: You can do better than that. Take a gap year: AJFHGRUINRIVNR!

It seems that whilst young people are going through different climates during various portions of their life, the older folk just like to stay where they are. Instead of embracing the new, they cling to the old. I know so many older people who have HD TV's with HD channels, but still watch standard definition all the time. I can't be the only one?

University has brought many positive changes to my life. For one, I've had to enforce stricter discipline on myself, so I don't have to worry about deadlines. Older people never had to do that. When my nan was young, her class struggled with algebra, so their teacher just gave up and taught something else. Ah, I wish the English Modernism lecturers had this same thought process. I'm still at the cliff edge, waiting for the right time to push myself off. I'll fall into whatever fate lies below. Hopefully, I won't get pushed by someone else. What I'm reaching at is this: If young people are getting constantly nagged and blamed for everything, then why do we expect any difference in attitude after the third-year. I don't. Our climate will soon be changing, and the only person that can make sure it's a good one is ourselves.

My Dad told me if I didn't do triple science I wouldn't get into university. Then he found out that in the same time slot as that lesson was aeronautical engineering, which came with the possibility of a job with a high paying salary. He changed his tune rather quickly on the whole triple science thing after that. In the end I chose graphics, and he threatened to go to the school and change it himself. He never did. All the options I chose in life, in varying climates, took me here. A third-year English student on his way to a degree. My choices. The cliff edge is mine. I won't push myself off, I'll get up and leap. I might get moaned at, I might get nagged at, but so what? The climate is what I make it, and so far, they haven't been polluted. Please, if you're going to critique me on these big decisions that I'm going to make then go ahead, but don't then go and praise the cat for not crapping on the sofa.

SURVIVING DEATH

KATIE STOTE

ILLUSTRATION XIN FU

At the age of 46, on holiday in a Spanish island with his wife Joanne, my uncle suffered a myocardial infarction, commonly known as a heart attack. He died before he reached the hospital. According to 'Harvard Health Publishing', in the year of his death, there was an estimated 94 percent chance of surviving a heart attack in the under 65. At 46, with odds of 94 to 6, Steve lost, and my family tree suffered a fatal blow, which brought it to its knees.

My grandparents live in a shoebox of a motorhome, the decoration of which seems to change with every season. One thing that has never changed over the years is the photo of Steve, he passed away before I had the chance to really know him. As long as I can remember, this photo has captured my interest. Who was he looking at? Where was he? So, I finally decided to call Mum and ask her about the photo. Before I could finish my questioning, she responded, "*Bath, he and Jo, went together.*" She explained how it was taken only weeks before he died, "*it might've been one of the last photos we have of him.*" Our conversation carried on, and for the first time I began to understand who Steve was, and the loss my mother experienced. This is her story, on surviving the death of her brother.

"*One thing that really surprised me, was how in the worst time of my life, we still managed to laugh…*" The day after the funeral, Sandra was sat in the garden with her family. As the radio played to itself in the background, they sat silently fanning themselves with scraps of paper, the heat was inescapable. The only thing more agitating than the invasive heat was the phantom fly which had made an appearance. *Buzzzz buzzzz*, Sandra lightly swatted the air around her head, *buzzzzz buzz zz*. It felt like it was inside her ear. *Buzzzzz Buzzzzz.* It began to hover near her brother's ear now. *"Bloody* fly!" Andy hissed as he grabbed the fan out of Sandra's hand and began looking around him, hunting the fly's whereabouts.

"No! Don't hit the fly! It could be Steve come back to visit us!" Sandra's mother cried.

"Steve? I'd hope he wouldn't come back as a bloody fly!" exclaimed her dad.

They all erupted in laughter, and then began to laugh even harder at the fact they were laughing at all, an unfamiliar sound of late. *"That's what grief does to you, you will experience a multitude of emotions, and you really feel thankful for those moments of relief, no matter how small they are."*

"Steve was more of a Dad figure to me, than my own dad..." Despite the twelve-year age gap, Sandra and Steve were incredibly close. Before he married and moved out at the age of seventeen, Sandra would be the first person he would give attention to when he returned home. They would eat ice-cream together, play in the garden, and as time progressed and she had children of her own, he would take them for days out, and sing them songs on his blue guitar.

When his marriage fell apart, and his life seemed the darkest it could be, he leaned on Sandra for support, numerous cups of tea and much-needed chats were had. Meanwhile, Andy distanced himself from his family. He became self-destructive, fuelled by addiction. Steve tried his best to keep him on the right track, scared of what would happen if no one else did, "that nipper will be the end of me" he would joke to Sandra.

When the phone rang late on the 24th of June 2002, Adam, Sandra's husband, took the call, "Oh my God" she heard him say. *"I was taking my socks off at the end of the bed, I just remember thinking, it's Dad, something has happened to Dad. Never in a million years... I'd only seen him a week before. It was the wrong order. It's not right. Not how things should be. It's just, yeah, it was a very, very strange time actually, quite bizarre, quite bizarre."* After the phone call, Sandra went straight to her parent's house. Her mother was doubled over on the floor, screaming, distorted in pain. Her father looked lost, so lost she was sure he would never be found again. When Andy arrived, he hugged Sandra tightly and said, just loud enough for her to hear, "it should've been me."

"Yeah, it should've been" she thought.

With time, Andy stepped into the role of big brother to Sandra; he ended his toxic marriage, got a house on his own, and eventually the drug addiction dissolved. Sandra's dad, having been raised in Naval boarding schools, always struggled with showing affection or emotion, and seemed to be softened by the death of his son. *"It's almost like through losing Steve, I gained the brother I had lost and the Dad I felt like I never really had."*

When I asked my mother how she got through her grief, she responded, *"you children."* She went on to explain that having to look after four young children, gave her normality in a time when everything felt strange. She had no option but to get up in the mornings because she had to get us fed, dressed and ready for the day. That was all she had to rely on for the first few months. Healing will be different for each person, but what is important to hold onto, is that with time you will begin to feel okay again… *"You learn to live around it. You never stop missing them, but you learn how to cope without them. In the past, when I was going through a difficult time, I would go and sit at his grave, and talk like we used too… but life pushes you forward, you can't just stop, and that's how you heal."*

THE SHADOW MEN

ELLA TAYLOR

We all love the idea of an adventure. We grow up reading books about children who enter a secret world through a wardrobe. We feel our way forward, desperate to take hold of something, completely unaware of what we are missing. Until we find it. We have a desire to seek the secret places. Those places that resist our road maps, our skyscrapers and our 4G. A place of our dreams that takes us beyond the realms of reality, into a world of unexplainable peace. Where the wind whistles to the trees and they swoon. Where your breathing slows…and your wild thoughts are released.

Dartmoor National Park has been described as a wilderness; vast and untamed. As humans, we have evolved into wilderness explorers. The chance to go somewhere new excites us; we thrive on the mystery of an adventure. A wilderness to me would be a place entirely untouched and undiscovered. A place that either shuts you out or traps you in. The reality is that Dartmoor attracts thousands of people a year because it is perfect for walking and exploring. The paths are well-worn, and they beckon the traveller to set foot on them. Although we love adventure, we also love our Timberlands and our Hunter wellies to be kept clean. I imagine that most of us would choose to explore on a path, rather than through a wet bog or an army of fern that would tangle the laces of our trainers. And if we choose a path, we are choosing to journey where the gravel has already been touched by someone else's feet. On my many trips to Dartmoor, I have come to realise that plenty of mystery lies in the history of all those feet, the feet that have walked before us, and the individual lives that they belong to. Nature invites us to discover its wild spaces, revealing the secret places that tell us tales of the past.

The path begins low in Princetown just past the fire station and a woodland, and it will lead us to Foggintor Quarry. With the first gate behind you, you are instantly surrounded by green. To your left and right there are horses. The right-hand horses are groomed and clothed with jackets. They are surrounded by a box of wire while you are free to roam. The left-hand horses have grown their hair long and they are scattered across the moorland. There is no end to their wanderings. I wonder if the right-hand horses want to be free from their box, or if the idea of joining the wanderers shivers the skin beneath their coats…

The path is flat and wide, painted with potholes and puddles. It climbs slow and steady following the curves of the moors. The eye wanders to the hills topped with tors, just before you reach the first bridge. Here you are exposed to the peaks, entirely vulnerable but not alone, for the wind catches your attention with howls and groans. You can only see the wind through a veil of hair, as it swoops forward and whips your skin. At this point on the path you don't see one thing; you see everything. It is as though someone has painted you into the landscape. Now you are walking with the moors. The October moors reveal shades that can only be described as golden-red, the kind of red that falls with the leaves in autumn or that gleams off the back of a fox. You can see the fox's red in the trees, the fern and the heather. With the sun still stirring, the tors wear a crown of mist and the dim light of morning whispers there is so much more to come.

THE SHADOW WITH NO CURE

AMY ROSSITER
ILLUSTRATION: XIN FU

Although I would like to think that I have developed in my knowledge of mental health and can deal with the sudden feeling of a panic attack better than I could as a teenager or even as I child, I still have sudden rushes of "bad adrenaline" where my immediate thought is "I am going to be sick" and "I need to get out." When I say "bad adrenaline" I mean in regards to feeling hyped and nervous as you would do before going on stage for example or what I imagine it would be like before you walk down the aisle getting married. However, "bad adrenaline" is when this feeling comes out of the blue, and feels uncontrollable. The excitement very quickly turns to panic. A rush of heat travels through as I am writing this, this experience happened just a couple of days ago.

I had arranged with one of my dearest friends to travel from Plymouth to London for one night to see one of my favourite musical theatre actresses Carrie Fletcher perform on the west end in *Heathers*. Before the trip, I was thrilled by the prospect of getting to see her live. However, as the days got closer to going, doubts started to arise in my head. I was in what felt like an endless void where deadlines were like crows picking at my eyeballs, and rehearsals for the panto were getting more intense. I felt stuck. Not only this, but I was broke. I had under one hundred pounds in my account at this point, and I was terrified that going to London would cost a fortune, just in travel and food. I had taken a gap year in order to save money for university and hopefully avoid being in an overdraft, however, the money I had saved was running out, and I was still in the mind frame that I could still spend money on things that I could this time last year. But the truth is, the money had disappeared. I still agreed to go to London though as it was a show that I desperately wanted to see and my worry of money had been evaded for the five minutes it took to book everything. However, after having booked it, a hundred questions rose in my head: How would I afford to live during university? Why before had I been so reckless with money? Why was I stupid enough to put myself in this situation. All of these thoughts made themselves at home in my mind for a few days, and ultimately led to me being overwhelmed, bordering on the feelings of depression. I recently came upon an article by Jennifer Lyke where she analyses the levels of anxiety suffered by adults and children based on their feelings towards their own "meaning of life." She went on to say "pursuing goals appears to enhance mental health by satisfying desires and defending against fears." Although this makes complete sense and I can imagine pursuing a goal and achieving it can give you a great sense of satisfaction rather than anxiety, I was riddled with interior goals at this point. I was juggling: two module deadlines, a dissertation deadline, rehearsals three nights a week, working for the university, very little money and stress of keeping to deadlines whilst travelling to London. By having too many goals to manage, it caused great stress, anxious and depressive thoughts. To top it all off my family were holidaying in St. Ives, as they do twice a year, every year and I was unable to visit them which I was really gutted about. So many overwhelming goals all at once certainly did not do me any favours with my mental health.

I am very blessed that I have an incredibly supportive family, boyfriend and his family that are people that I always turn to and always manage to put things into perspective for me. On this particular week, Ben had gone home so I was alone at university, and my parents, as I said, were on holiday. Not only was I struggling with separation anxiety, but I was also battling with the prospect of travelling and staying in London, a completely unfamiliar and intimidating place in my eyes. It was only when I read Thomas Ollendick's essay about separation anxiety where I felt I could relate to what he was saying that I realised that it was likely I was feeling this. He went on to say: "Separation Anxiety Disorder (SAD), one of the childhood anxiety disorders, is characterized by excessive anxiety when the subject is faced with separation from persons to whom he or she is attached."

An obvious idea when describing children, however, it definitely appeared to resonate with feelings I had at that point. Acknowledging what you are feeling is a great step to being able to answer back to those inner voices and start to find your feet again. If I ever feel in a bad way with my mental health, I always try to rationalise the thoughts I have: why are you feeling this way? Is there a trigger present? If so – eliminate it. I really had to go through this mind process whilst I was in the audience of *Heathers*.

Although I have performed on stage many times and have had to deal with show nerves, for some reason I get the same show nerves watching a show as if I was the one performing. Throughout the show, I was nervously checking behind my shoulders, as if a bee was buzzing around me, checking for the nearest "escape route". For my own piece of mind, I had to check which would be the easiest way to leave without causing a scene or by distracting the fewest amount of people. I could feel my temperature rise. My lips became dry whilst phlegm began to build in the back of my throat as though I was going to be sick.

Luckily, I made it through the whole performance without having to run out, but I was so angry at myself for allowing my anxiety to get so bad – I should have known better!

University of Plymouth Press